page 4

re	re	re	dis
over	over	de	de
dis	un	mis	mis

page 5

page 9

, , , ,

page 10

☑ ☑

☑ ☑

page 16

ent   ant   ent

ent   ant   ant

page 21

– how awful!   – it was amazing!

– unbelievable!   – I couldn't believe it!

page 23

hurried   **led**

pleasant   **colossal**

page 25

page 29

Leap Ahead Workbook

English

Home learning made fun

Leap Ahead

FASTER

FASTEST

FAST

igloobooks

Better or best?

Make your noun phrases even better by improving your adjectives. Add *er* and *est* to show how something compares to other things around it. Complete the table below.

Root word	Add -er	Add -est
large	larger	largest
long		
sharp		
pointy		
tiny		
rough		
smooth		
spiky		

Write two noun phrases about each alien on the dotted lines below using *er* and *est* adjectives. One has been done for you.

The pinkest alien with the roundest teeth...............................

....

....

....

....

....

Describing a monster!

Your monster has gone missing! You need to make a WANTED poster. Draw your monster in the box provided. Use exact descriptions of how he looks and how he acts or your monster may never be found!

Prefix mix

Find prefixes on your sticker sheet and add them to the root words below to create new words. Remember not all prefixes work with every word.

(sticker) appear   (sticker) honest   (sticker) write

(sticker) heard   (sticker) read   (sticker) crowding

(sticker) spell   (sticker) cover   (sticker) frost

(sticker) think   (sticker) believe   (sticker) construct

Once you've correctly identified the new words above, find them in the word search below. Look horizontally, vertically and diagonally.

r	e	a	p	p	e	a	r	g	c	u	o
e	k	s	r	m	o	q	e	t	f	n	v
r	r	l	q	n	m	s	w	z	g	c	e
e	m	i	s	h	e	a	r	d	p	o	r
a	u	d	z	e	a	j	i	w	j	v	t
d	e	f	r	o	s	t	t	o	h	e	h
t	j	m	i	s	s	p	e	l	l	r	i
d	e	c	o	n	s	t	r	u	c	t	n
n	p	d	i	s	h	o	n	e	s	t	k
d	i	s	b	e	l	i	e	v	e	v	b
o	v	e	r	c	r	o	w	d	i	n	g

Answers on page 32

Homophones

Homophones are words that sound the same but are spelt differently, for example: *there/their/they're*.

For numbers 1 and 2 below, find and match a sticker from the sticker sheet to the correct homophone. Then, for each one, write a sentence using both homophones.

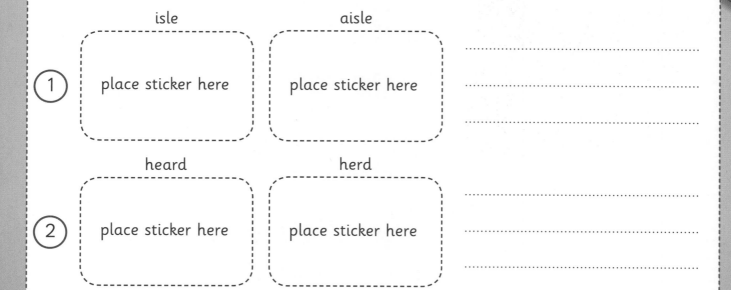

isle | aisle

① place sticker here | place sticker here | ....

heard | herd

② place sticker here | place sticker here | ....

For numbers 3 and 4 below, draw a picture to match the word. Then, for each one, write a sentence using both homophones.

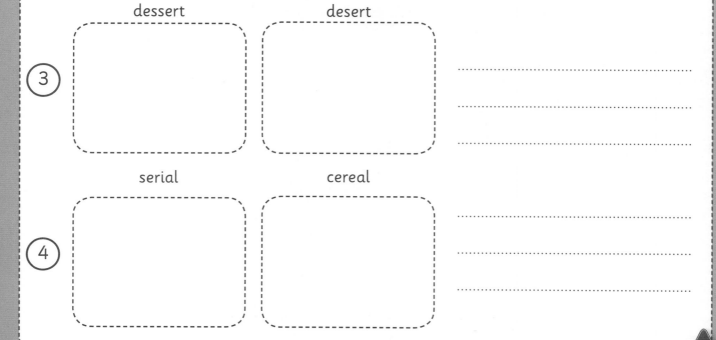

dessert | desert

③ ....

serial | cereal

④ ....

Answers on page 32

Fronted adverbials

Fronted adverbials help to link from one sentence to the next. They are also used to introduce paragraphs. Read the recount about a trip to the swimming pool. Find all the fronted adverbials in the text and underline each one.

On Saturday, a group of friends were taking a trip to the swimming pool. First, they got on the busy bus, which was full of passengers. On the bus, they chatted about what they were going to do at the pool. Everyone was so excited!

At last, they arrived. Right outside the pool, the bus ground to a halt. Finally, the four joyful friends hopped off. Inside, they queued for their tickets. Suddenly, they heard a groan. "Oh no! I've forgotten my trunks," shouted Ben from the back of the queue.

Sort the fronted adverbials into the table below. Add some more of your own, too.

Time	Place	Number

Answers on page 32

Dear Diary

Write a diary entry about a trip you have been on with your friends. Use fronted adverbials to link your sentences and introduce your paragraphs. To write an effective diary, imagine you are talking to your best friend. Give your opinion and talk about things you enjoyed or didn't like as well as writing what you have done. You might use questions and exclamations but remember not to use speech! After writing your diary entry, draw a picture in the box.

Relative clauses

Read the sentences below. Draw circles around the nouns.

The dog chased the pigeon.

One evening, Catherine caught the bus.

The friends loved going to the bowling alley.

The cat walked past the car.

The cyclist sped over the hill.

Answers on page 32

Relative clauses give more information about nouns. A relative clause starts with a relative pronoun (*who, which, when, where, that, whose*). A relative clause can be written about any of the nouns in the sentences you have just read.

For example:
The dog, <u>who was ferocious</u>, chased the pigeon.
The dog chased the pigeon, <u>which had a sore wing</u>.

Add relative clauses to the two sentences below. Choose an appropriate relative pronoun.

One night, Catherine, ...

...., caught the bus.

The friends loved going to the bowling alley, ...

....

A pair of commas

Read the sentences below. Notice where the relative clause goes. Look at the commas, which mark a relative clause when it is in the middle of a sentence.

Kayleigh loved her street dance lesson.

Kayleigh, who was a great dancer, loved her street dance lesson.

Can you add the commas in the following sentences? Use the comma stickers on the sticker sheet.

The house which was abandoned stood in the middle of the forest.

The giraffe when it ran looked gangly and clumsy.

Write three sentences of your own using relative clauses and commas.

....

....

....

....

....

....

....

....

Answers on page 32

Ending in *cial* or *tial*?

These two suffixes sound the same. Remember that *cial* is common after a vowel letter and *tial* is common after a consonant letter. There are some exceptions, such as: *financial, commercial, provincial* and *initial*.

Draw a link to match the beginnings of these words to the correct suffixes.

offi   cial

spe   tial

confiden   cial

artifi   tial

par   cial

essen   tial

Answers on page 32

Follow the rules (and the exceptions) to check which words below are spelt correctly. Cross out and change any incorrect spellings. Put a tick sticker next to correct spellings.

finantial   provintial   initial

benifitial   crucial   partial

confidencial   marcial   commercial

Answers on page 32

In the news

Look at what is happening in the pictures below. Write newspaper headlines for the disasters. Make sure your headlines have no more than 7 words. Choose the words carefully to attract the attention of the reader.

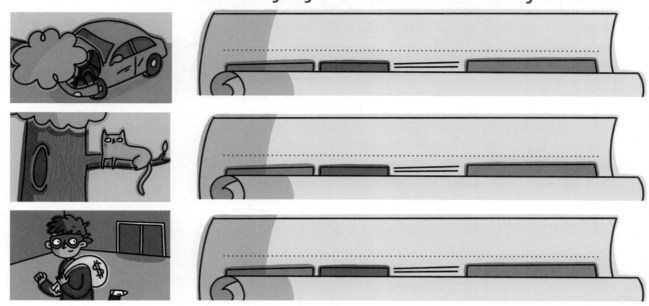

Read the newspaper report below.

On Thursday night, in the village of Greenton, a young couple narrowly escaped disaster. Severe winds of over 35 miles an hour had **got up** around the region. Some households reported losing roof tiles and several small trees had blown over in gardens. People were out in the wind **making safe** fences and bins.

After their dinner, Mr and Mrs Stone had set off in their car to check on Mrs Stone's parents. Around 6:30pm, they drove down Main Street when a sudden gust of wind uprooted a tree on the road side. The tree swayed and **shook** before falling down just in front of Mr and Mrs Stone's car, taking the bumper and number plate off. Luckily, the couple **answered** quickly, stopped the car and made a safe exit.

Evaluate whether the bold words in the report are correct for the situation. Look at the multiple choice selection below and put a ring around the one that makes the information in the report clear.

got up	built up	gathered	grown	developed
making safe	securing	fixing	pushing	sticking
shook	fell	creaked	leaned	trembled
answered	reacted	responded	jumped	went

A newspaper report

Read the report then record the main details by answering the questions.

On Saturday 1st May, Mrs Johnson reported her cat missing at the local police station in Bigtown. The police visited the area close to Mrs Johnson's house later that afternoon. Meowing was heard in the woods by two dog walkers. The police investigated and found little Fluffy (Mrs Johnson's cat) stuck up a large oak tree on the edge of the woods. With a little help from Stuart the builder and his ladder, the cat was rescued and safely returned to Mrs Johnson.

1. **Who has lost something?** ....

2. **What is missing?** ....

3. **When did she report it missing?** ....

4. **Where was it reported missing?** ....

5. **Why was it missing?** ....

....

Answers on page 32

Plan to write your own news report in a similar style to the ones you have read.

who	what	when	where	why

Use the details in the table to write your newspaper report. Think about how you will introduce it and make sure you write an ending to finish the report. Try writing expanded noun phrases and relative clauses to add extra details in your report to make it interesting for the reader.

PARENT TIP: Check your child writes the report in the past tense and uses the third person (*he, she, they, it*). They may want to add eyewitness accounts in direct or reported speech (e.g. *The couple said they were shocked and scared*).

13

Suffixes

You can turn many nouns and adjectives into verbs by adding the right suffix. Tick the boxes in the table below to choose the correct suffix, then write out the new verb.

Root word (adjective or noun)	-ate	-ise	-ify	Write out the new word (verb)
glory			√	glorify
elastic				
civil				
class				
active				
pure				
advert				
personal				

Do you notice any patterns when you add the suffix? Look closely at 'glory' and 'active'. What did you have to do?

....

....

Some of the words below are wrong. Can you cross out the incorrect ones and write the correct spelling above them?

personalify   civilise   advertate

activate   classify   glorise

Answers on page 32

PARENT TIP: Write out root words (e.g. *personal*, *civil* and *class*) on separate pieces of paper. Write out the suffixes *ise*, *ify* and *ate* on separate pieces of paper. Scatter them face-down on the table. Take turns to choose a word card and a suffix card. If they match, you get one point. If they don't match, put them face-down back on the table. The person with the most points after 5 minutes wins.

Correct commas

Add commas to the sentences in the correct places. You need to use commas to separate activities in a list, otherwise the meaning will be muddled! Can you imagine a kangaroo watching bounces or a snake dancing the twist?

The kangaroo watches bounces and hides in the bushes.

The python dances twists and turns.

The lion hunts shelters and lies in wait for prey.

Commas are also needed to mark the boundary between a main clause and a subordinate clause. Tick the sentences below that have commas in the correct place.

As the safari car drove through the jungle, the animals looked on.		As the safari car drove, through the jungle the animals looked on.	
As the chameleon watched the rain, it changed colour.		As the, chameleon watched the rain it changed colour.	
The zebra has black and white stripes, because it needs to camouflage from predators.		The zebra has black, and white stripes because it needs to camouflage from predators.	
Before the baby elephant could, move out the way the mother elephant squirted water over it!		Before the baby elephant could move out the way, the mother elephant squirted water over it!	

Answers on page 32

Competent spelling

These lily pads each have a root word which can end in the suffix *ent* or *ant*. The frog stickers on your sticker sheet have suffixes on them. Place each frog on the correct lily pad.

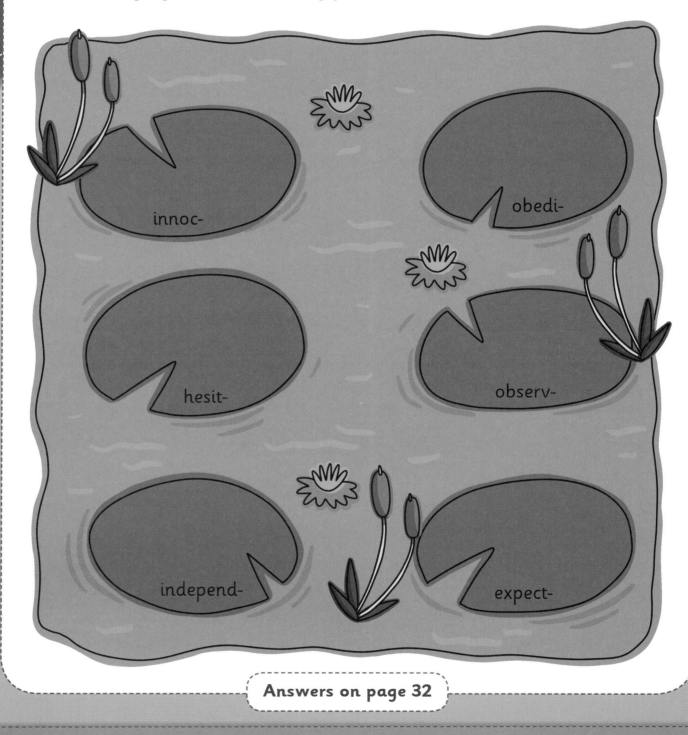

innoc-

obedi-

hesit-

observ-

independ-

expect-

Answers on page 32

PARENT TIP: Remind your child to choose *ent/ence/ency* following a soft *c*, *g* or *qu*. Choose *ant/ance/ancy* if there is a clear *a* sound as in *substance*. Remember that there are some exceptions.

Analysing a story

Predict what will happen in the story by looking at the three pictures below. Write your prediction on the dotted lines below, then read the story to see if you are correct.

....

....

Read the story below, then answer the questions.

Will had got a new game for his birthday. He hadn't opened it straight away as he was waiting to play it with his best friend, Sam. One evening, when Sam had come around for tea, the boys decided to open the dark and mysterious looking game. When they opened it, the boys were sure they heard a cannon firing in the distance. "That's odd!" thought Will. Once the box was opened, they quickly set up the game and Will rolled to go first. As he let go of the dice, the world began to spin. Both boys were lifted off the ground and the house turned to sky around them. Will could feel his heart beating loudly in his chest and questions were running through his mind. What had happened?

Suddenly, the sky settled. Sam and Will found themselves standing upright. The clouds and mist cleared away. At once, they both looked up and in front of them was a castle. Not just any castle – a castle that was at least twenty times bigger than them and had loud music coming from it! Sam looked over at his friend. "What should we do?" he asked.

Why didn't Will open the game straight away?

....

Find and copy the phrase in paragraph one that gives you a clue that there will be a castle in the game.

....

What was special about the castle?

....

Creating cohesion

You can use adverbials of time, place and manner to link across and within paragraphs of writing. Look at the adverbials below and draw a line from each one to the correct type.

firstly

finally

in the afternoon   place

at dusk   time

secondly   number

around the corner

thirdly

Choose appropriate adverbials from the cloud to link the sentences in this paragraph together.

_____, the sky went black. _____, the thunder roared and the lightning filled every corner of the sky. _____, the friends took shelter from the storm. They weren't sure what to do next. "_____, we need to find somewhere safe and dry," thought one of them. _____, they set off, staying under the cover of the trees to find somewhere to sleep for the night.

firstly
suddenly
under the trees
a few minutes later
up above them

Answers on page 32

PARENT TIP: Take it in turns with your child to say sentences to make up a story. Start each sentence with one of the adverbials from the cloud above. When it is your turn, you can take the story in any direction you like!

Planning a short story

Here are some ideas for characters and settings of a story.

Characters:	Settings:
An alien	Another planet
Two friends	A forest
A hooded figure	An abandoned school
A broken toy soldier	A castle
A knight	A shopping centre

Choose one character and one setting from the lists above, then decide on your own plot. Write sentences to describe your characters and setting. Try to use a mixture of short sentences and sentences joined with conjunctions. Can you use a relative clause?

Conjunctions:
because
when
after
while
as
but
and

....

....

....

....

....

....

....

....

....

Which is your favourite sentence? Why?

....

....

....

Writing a short story

Write a short story (around 100 words) based on your plan on page 19. Use the checklist below to make sure you include elements you've learnt about in this workbook.

Checklist:

☐ I've used adverbials for time. ☐ I've used adverbials for place.

☐ I've used a range of conjunctions. ☐ I've used simple sentences.

☐ I've used relative clauses.

....

....

....

....

....

....

....

....

....

....

....

....

....

....

Dashes

Dashes can be used to add comments and extra information at the end of a sentence. Use the stickers to add a comment or point of view to each of the main clauses below.

At the weekend, I went to a trampoline park with my friend ⟨ place sticker here ⟩

He collected a whole set of cards ⟨ place sticker here ⟩

The little girl fell ill on her birthday and missed her party ⟨ place sticker here ⟩

The boys broke the world record for an elastic band ball ⟨ place sticker here ⟩

Now write an email to a friend. Use dashes at the end of sentences to add extra information or a point of view.

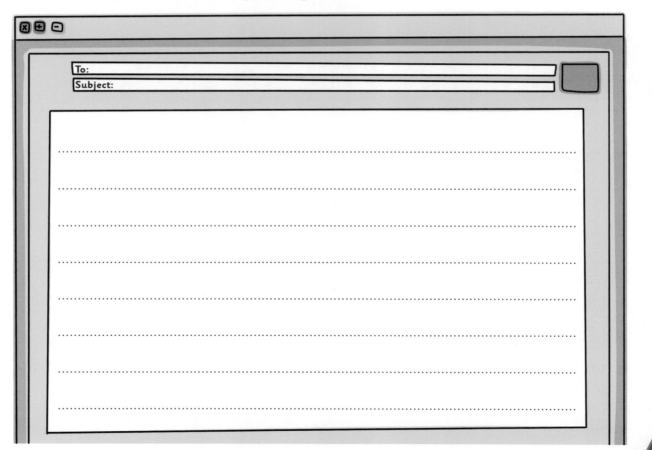

To:

Subject:

Silent letter crossword

All the answers to the clues have a silent letter in them. Find the answers to the clues and fill them into the crossword.

ACROSS

1 across: An upright cylindrical pillar which supports an arch or roof.

2 across: A landmass surrounded by water.

3 across: A feeling of uncertainty.

4 across: A piece of cutlery used for cutting.

DOWN

1 down: A man who serves a lord on horseback wearing armour.

2 down: A baby sheep.

3 down: Very serious and formal.

Answers on page 32

Choose the best word

Read the passage of writing below about a school trip to the museum. The writer has used some weak vocabulary (in bold). Select a sticker with a better word choice and stick it in place to improve the text.

Yesterday, Class 5 visited the city museum.

Firstly, the class got ready with coats, packed lunches and partners – everyone got to sit by their friend! When they arrived at the museum, they **went** excitedly to the front doors. The children were met by a **nice** museum assistant who showed them around all of the exhibits.

After that, the teacher **took** the class to the dinosaur gallery. They looked at the ichthyosaurs and plesiosaurs before finally spotting the **big** T-rex standing ahead of them. It was scary!

Read the next part of the text and look out for spelling, grammar and punctuation mistakes. Correct them with a coloured pen or pencil.

The next gallery they visited was full off stone tools. Everyone Enjoyed lucking at the flints and arrowheads.

At lunchtime, the class ate their packed lunches outside in the sunshine The museum had lots of picnic benchs for them to sit on whil they were eating their lunch

In the afternoon the class made observasions off the Ancient Greek artefacts. The vase paintings were very detailed. Their was so many jewels and objects to look at!

Exciting cities

Read these texts about two cities and then answer the questions about them.

New York city is in New York State (USA). Although it is a very well known city, it is not the capital city of America (Washington DC is). 8.4 million people live across the 5 boroughs of New York. These boroughs are called: Brooklyn, Bronx, Queens, Staten Island and Manhattan (which is the most visited borough). New York has several famous landmarks including the Statue of Liberty, which was a gift from France, situated on Liberty Island. Brooklyn Bridge, which connects Manhattan with Brooklyn, is one of the world's oldest suspension bridges. It opened in 1883.

Nairobi is the capital city of Kenya (a country situated in Eastern Africa). As well as having a busy metropolitan centre, the city has Nairobi National Park, which is a large game reserve known for breeding endangered black rhinos and home to giraffes, zebras and lions. Nairobi is the largest city between Cairo (Egypt) and Johannesburg (South Africa). Around 50 million people live in the country of Kenya, with just under 3 million people living in Nairobi. Nairobi is full of skyscrapers and world-class restaurants. Interestingly, Kenya's greatest export is tea!

1. What is the capital city of America? ....

2. How many boroughs are in New York City? ....

3. Which borough has the most visitors? ....

4. What opened in 1883? ....

5. How many more people live in New York than Nairobi? ....

6. What makes Nairobi special? ....

7. Where is Nairobi? ....

8. Name 3 large cities in East Africa. ....

Answers on page 32

Parenthesis

You can leave out the relative pronoun in a relative clause when adding extra information if you add commas or brackets. This is called parenthesis and it sometimes makes a sentence easier to read. Look at the examples below.

Paris, **which is the capital city of France,** is in the north of the country.

Paris **(capital city of France)** is in the north of the country.

Paris, **the capital city of France,** is in the north of the country.

Put the stickers from the sticker sheet next to the correct sentences then write your own parentheses in these sentences.

place sticker here | T-rex (..) lived in the Cretaceous period.

place sticker here | The local train (..) leaves at 2:30pm daily.

place sticker here | Trainers (..) are comfortable to wear when playing sport.

place sticker here | Swans (..) are extremely beautiful creatures.

PARENT TIP: Parenthesis works really well with factual information. It can be used to give extra information, to explain something or give a definition. See if you can find examples in a newspaper or magazine article to show your child.

25

Using brackets

Draw four of your best friends in the boxes below. Describe your friends using brackets to add extra information.

Paragraphs

As well as making sure each paragraph is linked to the next, you also need to link each sentence to the next so that your writing flows. You can use adverbs for this.

Read the sentences below. They are not in order. Your first job is to decide an order for them, then choose adverbs to link each one to the next. Write the sentences into a paragraph in your chosen order with adverbs (from the circle) to link them together.

Lions live in Africa in savannahs or grasslands.

A baby lion is called a cub and it will live up to 16 years in the wild.

Lions are large mammals belonging to the cat family.

They are very sociable animals and they live in groups called prides.

Female lions do most of the hunting while the male lions patrol to protect their territory.

furthermore
finally certainly
additionally
moreover
firstly
also

....

....

....

....

....

....

....

....

Big spelling test

Can you spell all of these words? You have practised all the rules for them in this book. Ask an adult to test you or write out your spellings then check them yourself.

government

accommodate

appreciate

mischievous

especially

disastrous

opportunity

environment

profession

muscle

observation

knight

aisle

cereal

independence

hesitant

confidential

special

Sub-headings

Read each passage of text and write an appropriate sub-heading for each one, then a short introduction underneath the sub-heading to summarise what the paragraph is about. Finally, find a sticker that matches the topic, stick it in the box and write a caption underneath it.

....

....

Many people believe children in Year 5 should not have mobile phones because they may lose them or smash them. Teachers think it is unfair for some children to own phones and not others. Some parents think it is hard to manage ten year olds on social media. However, Year 5 children feel they are useful for keeping in contact, especially when they walk home on their own.

place sticker here

....

....

....

Cricket is a game played by people of all ages. The game involves two teams (a batting team and a bowling team). The game requires several pieces of equipment: bats, a hard ball and stumps with bails placed on top. It is played on a large, circular field. The team that scores the most runs is the winner.

place sticker here

....

....

....

There are many different types of ride at theme parks including rollercoasters and water rides. Theme parks are enjoyed by all members of the family, not just for the rides but for the surroundings, gardens and food. Visiting theme parks can be expensive but also a great deal of fun.

place sticker here

....

My fact file

You have been asked to create a guide about an animal found in the jungle. Plan out an informative report on a jungle animal of your choice.

The questions below will help you plan your guide. Plan each paragraph using the boxes below.

What does the creature look like?
Where does it live?
What does it eat?
What does the creature do during the day?
What does the creature do during the night?
Do you have an interesting fact to end?

Subheading	
Notes	

Subheading	
Notes	

Subheading	
Notes	

Now it's time to write your report. Remember to include: sub-headings for each paragraph, adverbs for cohesion, relative clauses, brackets, dashes and commas. Draw a picture of the animal in the empty box.

Answers

Page 2: Better or best?
large/larger/largest; long/longer/longest; sharp/sharper/sharpest; pointy/pointier/pointiest; tiny/tinier/tiniest; rough/rougher/roughest; smooth/smoother/smoothest; spiky/spikier/spikiest

Page 4: Prefix mix
reappear, misheard, misspell, overthink, dishonest, reread, uncover, disbelieve, rewrite, overcrowding, defrost, deconstruct

r	e	a	p	p	e	a	r	g	c	u	o
e	k	s	r	m	o	q	e	t	f	n	v
r	r	l	q	n	m	s	w	z	g	c	e
e	m	i	s	h	e	a	r	d	p	o	r
a	u	d	z	e	a	j	i	w	j	v	t
d	e	f	r	o	s	t	t	o	h	e	h
t	j	m	i	s	s	p	e	l	l	r	i
d	e	c	o	n	s	t	r	u	c	t	n
n	p	d	i	s	h	o	n	e	s	t	k
d	i	s	b	e	l	i	e	v	e	v	b
o	v	e	r	c	r	o	w	d	i	n	g

Page 5: Homophones
1. isle = island sticker / aisle = shopping aisle sticker
2. heard = ear sticker / herd = group of cows sticker
3. dessert = e.g. a sweet treat eaten after dinner / desert = e.g. a vast dry land
4. serial = e.g. a series of TV shows or books / cereal = e.g. a bowl of food eaten for breakfast

Page 6: Fronted adverbials
Time: On Saturday / At last / Suddenly
Place: On the bus / Right outside the pool / Inside
Number: First / Finally

Page 8: Relative clauses
Nouns: dog / pigeon / Catherine / bus / friends / bowling alley / cat / car / cyclist / hill

Page 9: A pair of commas
The house, which was abandoned, stood in the middle of the forest.
The giraffe, when it ran, looked gangly and clumsy.

Page 10: Ending in *cial* or *tial*?
official / special / confidential / artificial / partial / essential
Correct: initial / crucial / partial / commercial
Incorrect: finantial / provintial / benifitial / confidencial / marcial

Page 12: A newspaper report
1. Mrs Johnson. **2.** Her cat. **3.** Saturday 1st May. **4.** The local police station. **5.** It was stuck up a large oak tree.

Page 14: Suffixes
glory / -ify / glorify; elastic / -ate / elasticate; civil / -ise / civilise; class / -ify / classify; active / -ate / activate; pure / -ify / purify; advert / -ise / advertise; personal / -ise / personalise

Page 15: Correct commas
The kangaroo watches, bounces and hides in the bushes.
The python dances, twists and turns.
The lion hunts, shelters and lies in wait for prey.

As the safari car drove through the jungle, the animals looked on.	√	As the safari car drove, through the jungle the animals looked on.	
As the chameleon watched the rain, it changed colour.	√	As the, chameleon watched the rain it changed colour.	
The zebra has black and white stripes, because it needs to camouflage from predators.		The zebra has black, and white stripes because it needs to camouflage from predators.	√
Before the baby elephant could, move out the way the mother elephant squirted water over it!		Before the baby elephant could move out the way, the mother elephant squirted water over it!	√

Page 16: Competent spelling
innocent / obedient / hesitant / independent / expectant / observant

Page 18: Creating cohesion
Place: around the corner / **Time:** in the afternoon, at dusk / **Number:** firstly, secondly, thirdly, finally

There are several appropriate answers for this activity. One example is below:
Suddenly, the sky went black. Up above them, the thunder roared and the lightning filled every corner of the sky. Under the trees, the friends took shelter from the storm. They weren't sure what to do next. "Firstly, we need to find somewhere safe and dry," thought one of the friends. A few minutes later, they set off, staying under the cover of the trees to find somewhere to sleep for the night.

Page 22: Silent letter crossword
1 down: knight / 2 down: lamb / 3 down: solemn / 1 across: column / 2 across: island / 3 across: doubt / 4 across: knife

Page 23: Choose the best word
went = hurried / nice = pleasant / took = led / big = colossal

The next gallery they visited was full **of** stone tools. Everyone enjoyed **looking** at the flints and arrowheads. At lunchtime, the class ate their packed lunches outside in the sunshine. The museum had lots of picnic **benches** for them to sit on **while** they were eating their lunch. In the afternoon, the class made **observations of** the Ancient Greek artefacts. The vase paintings were very detailed. **There were** so many jewels and objects to look at!

Page 24: Exciting cities
1. Washington DC
2. 5
3. Manhattan
4. Brooklyn Bridge
5. 5.4 million
6. It has a National Park. It has skyscrapers. It has world-class restaurants.
7. Kenya
8. Nairobi, Cairo, Johannesburg